MOTHER

IN

HIEROGLYPHICS.

Boston
Houghton Mifflin Company
1962

MOTHER GOOSE IN HIEROGLYPHICS was first published in 1849 by the Boston firm of Frederick A. Brown & Co. whose offices were at 29 Cornhill. The author had modestly withheld his name, but the copyright was taken out in the name of George S. Appleton. A copy of the book was recently rediscovered and is now being reprinted in a facsimile edition by the Nimrod Press. All of the original book has been conscientiously preserved including the misspelling on the cover.

The introduction to the first edition, which appears on the opposite page (and which makes sales copy of today seem pallid fare) is surely introduction enough. There are three things, however, that remain to be pointed out.

1. There is a ⚷ in the back of the book for those who have lost or not yet discovered the art of reading hieroglyphics.

2. *Spits* and *Pudding Sticks* are not in such common use today, nor is a pitcher usually referred to as a *Ewer*. But no harm, the reader will find that the passage of time has only added its own flavor to these puzzles.

3. We cannot supply you (at the present time, anyway) with the wares so intriguingly advertised in the back of this book. But if the wee ones keep themselves quiet (as the author suggests in his introduction) by tearing up this one, we can provide you with any number of new copies that are just as fresh and charming as the day the book was first published, well over a century ago. *j1421*

A NIMROD PRESS BOOK

Library of Congress Catalog Card Number: 62-15650   Printed in the U.S.A.

It is often said that folks now-a-days are a deal wiser than their fathers and grandfathers; but I don't think so; for who has ever written tales like Mother Goose, Mother Hubbard, and Mother What's-her-Name, that lived a great while ago? and books for children, too, little dears. How many of them owe their lives to the influence of their soothing songs and lullabys! The world would not have been half peopled had not these old sages once lived and written their invaluable little books for children.

When the doctor sends for physic for a nervous little chick, make a mistake, and go to the bookseller's and buy Mother Goose in Hieroglyphics; that's what is wanted—a pretty book, written with pictures, as they wrote in Egypt a long while ago, when folks knew something,—about the time when Mother Goose herself was a little gosling.

Yes, buy one of these little books, and when it is torn up, buy another, and another, till the wee ones are old enough to read Robinson Crusoe, and the like. My word for it, there is nothing like books with pictures, to keep children quiet; and this is the best that was ever written, as everybody knows.

Little Jack er sat in a er,

 a Christmas

He put in his and pulled out a

Oh! what a great  am

Pussy  pussy where have you been?

 've been to London, to see the

Pussy pussy  what did you there?

 frightened a little under a

There were  went to

 run a

The  did  the bumble

And scratched him in the

Ride a  to Charing

To see an jump on a white

With  on her fingers, and on her toes,

And she shall have wherever she goes.

Robert  with fine,

 you  this  of mine?

Yes, good  that

As as any other

Here's a and there's a

Now, good sir,  will do.

A **a** bouncing **B**

The 's in the and she can't C.

The little black 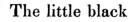 ran round the

And set the  a-roaring,

And drove the in the

Who set the  a-rowing,

And scared the  upon a

Who cracked his throat in

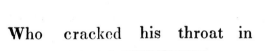

 the   the mare,

And let the little go

Who comes here?

What do you  ? A pint of

Where is your ?  forgot.

Then get you you drunken

To  to bed, says sleepy

Let 's stay awhile, says

Put on the says greedy-gut,

We 'll sup fore we go.

When  was a little

My mother kept me

Now I am a

And fit to serve the

I handle a

I smoke a

I kiss a pretty

At at

Up in the green  there is a green

The finest of that ever see;

The are ripe and ready to fall.

And **Reuben** and **Robin** shall gather them

B

Hush **a** bye upon the

When the wind blows, the  will rock;

When the  breaks, the will fall,

And down cradle, baby, and

Hey ! diddle, diddle, the  and the

The  jumped over the

The little laughed to  the sport,

And the   away with the

1, 2, buckle my 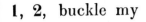   **3, 4,** shut the

5, 6, pick up   **7, 8,** hang the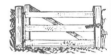

9, 10, a good fat    **11, 12,** ring the

13, 14, draw the   **15, 16,** go to

17, 18, to hear the   **19, 20,** that's a

Little  blue, come blow your

The are in the meadows, the  in the corn;

Is this the  you mind your  ?

Under the  fast

There was an sold puddings and s,

She went to the  and the dust flew in her

While through the  to she meets,

She ever Hot Pies ! Hot

Tom, Tom, the 's son,

Stole a  and away he

The  was eat, and Tom was

And Tom   down the street.

There was an old **wh**o lived in a

She had so many  she did n't know what to do.

She gave them some broth, without any

She them soundly, and put them to

The  in the came down too soon,

To inquire the   Norridge;

The in the South, burnt his

With  cold porridge.

Miss Jane had a and a was  it

She opened the he was out  a minute.

The  him jump and run under the

And the said, catch him, as soon as able.

Sing a  of sixpence, a full of

Four and twenty baked in a

When the  was opened, the began to sing,

And was n't this a dainty to set before the

The  was in the parlor, counting out his

The was in the  eating bread and honey;

The was in the  hanging out the

There came a little black and nipt off her

Baa! Baa! Black  have you any wool?

Yes marry, have  three s full.

1 for my Master, and 1 for my

And 1 for the little that lives in the lane.

 a   doodle   doo !

My has lost her

My   Master 's his

And   knows what   to   **do.**

Hiccory, diccory,

The mouse ran up the

The struck **1**, and down he

Hiccory, diccory,

Jemmy Jed went to a

And made of a ted of his

An came out, and flew about,

And Jemmy Jed, up and fled.

Was n't Jemmy Jed a staring

Born in the  to be scared by an

Round about, round about, gooseberry

My father loves good and so do

c

The two grey s, and the grey s' mother,

 went over the  together.

The  broke down, they fell in;

May the  go with you, says **Tom Bolin.**

There was a   our

And he was wondrous wise,

He  into a bramble

And scratched out both his

And when he his   were out,

With his might and main,

He  ed into another

And scratched them  again.

As  was going to sell my

 met a thief with bandy

Bandy and crooked

I  him up, and he fell on his

The  came in with the

The little  rocked the

The jumped up on the

To see the swallow the

The  that stood behind the

Threw the  on the floor.

Oddsplut! said the can't  agree,

I 'm the constable, bring them me.

Charley s good cake and

Charley s good D.

Charley s to kiss the

When they are clean and  D.

Hark ! Hark ! The  do bark,

The have come to

$$\begin{array}{r} 24 \\ 6 \\ 12)\overline{144}(12 \\ 12 \\ \overline{24} \\ 24 \end{array}$$ in rags, and some  tags,

And $$\begin{array}{r} 85 \\ 9 \\ 3)\overline{765} \\ \overline{255} \end{array}$$ in velvet s.

s   **in**   the   garden,   catch   them,   Towser ;

 in the  field, run  run ;

s in the cream-pot, run  run girls ;

Fire   on   the  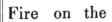 boys, run.

Diddle, diddle, dumpling, my  John,

Went to  with his on,

One off, and one on

Diddle, diddle, dumpling, my John.

Smiling  y

Come and buy my little

 made of ginger

And sugar  painted red.

There was an  tossed up  a blanket,

70 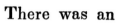 as high as the

What she did there, cannot

 her  she carried a

Old   woman,   old   old   woman,   says

Whither,   O   whither,   O   whither      high ?

To   sweep   the   from   the

And      shall   back   again,   by   and   by.

The in the wilderness asked me,

How many grew in the

I answered him as  thought good,

As many red as grew in the

Bye bunting, Father 's gone a

Mother 's gone a  Sister 's gone a silking

And Brother 's gone to get a  skin,

To wrap the  bunting

Little  **Nory** told me a story,

How he tried  to ride,

 and by his side,

leaden s and

 puzzles,

Now he's drest in and

The is red ; the is blue ;

 are pretty, and so are

 a bye   is green,

Father 's a  Mother 's a

Betty 's a and wears a gold

And Johnny 's a and for the

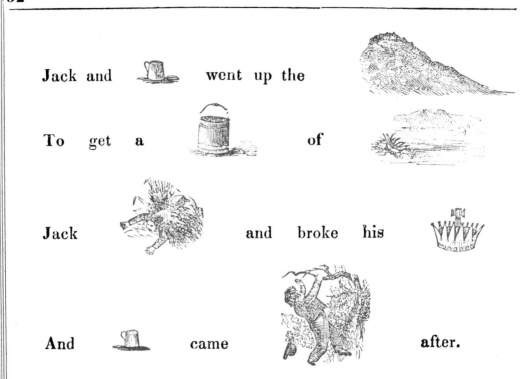

Jack and 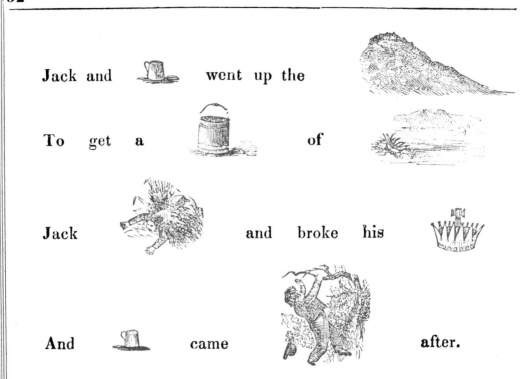 went up the

To get a of

Jack and broke his

And came after.

Sweep! sweep!

Sweep up, from the bottom to the

Without a or a

Sweep, O

 and  **come** out to play,

The does shine as bright **as day,**

Leave your  and leave your

And meet **your**  **in the**

There was an lived under the

And if she's gone, she lives there still.

Baked she sold, and cranberry

And she's the old that never told lies.

16. Can, Musket, Can, Pipe, Can, Girl, Clock, Night.
17. Orchard, Tree, Apples, Yew, Apples, Awl.
18. Baby, Tree, Top, Cradle, Bough, Cradle, Tumble, Awl.
19. Cat, Fiddle, Cow, Moon, Dog, Sea, Dish, Ran, Spoon.
20. Shoe, Door, Sticks, Gate, Hen, Bell, Curtain, Meeting, Preaching, Plenty.
21. Boy, Horn, Sheep, Cows, Way, Sheep, Hay-stack, Asleep.
22. Old Woman, Pies, Mill, Eyes, Street, Awl, Cries, Pies.
23. Piper, Pig, Run, Pig, Beat, Crying.
24. Old Woman, Shoe, Children, Bread, Whipped, Awl, Bed.
25. Man, Moon, Weigh, Toe, Man, Mouth, Eating, Plum.
26. Bag, Mouse, Inn, Bag, Inn, Cat, Saw, Table, Dog, Puss, Ewer.
27. Song, Bag, Rye, Blackbirds, Pie, Birds, Dish, King.
28. King, Money, Queen, Kitchen, Maid, Garden, Clothes, Bird, Nose.
29. Sheep, Eye, Bag, Dame, Boy, Lane.
30. Cock, Dame, Shoe, Lost, Fiddlestick, Knot.
31. Dock, Clock, Clock, Ran, Dock.

PAGE

32. Inn, Shed, Straw, Bed, Owl, Stakes.

33. Fool, Woods, Owl, Pie, Ale, Eye.

34. Kit, Kit, Awl, Bridge, Bridge, Awl, Rats.

35. Man, Inn, Town, Jumped, Bush, Eyes.

36. Saw, Eyes, Awl, Jump, Bush, Inn.

37. Eye, Eggs, Eye, Legs, Legs, Toes, Tripped, Nose.

38. Sow, Saddle, Pig, Cradle, Dish, Table, Pot, Ladle.

39. Spit, Door, Pudding-stick, Gridiron, Ewe, Head, Toe.

40. Loves, Ale, Loves, Candy, Loves, Girls, Handy.

41. Dogs, Beggars, Town, Sum, Inn, Sum, Gown.

42. Hog, Cows, Corn, Boys, Cat, Girls, Mountains, Run.

43. Sun, Bed, Trowsers, Stocking, Stocking, Sun.

44. Girls, Rose, Boys, Toys, Monkeys, Bread, Horses.

45 Old Woman, Inn, Moon, Eye, Tell, Butt, Inn, Hand, Broom.

46. Woman, Eye, Sow, Cobwebs, Sky, Eye, Bee.

47. Man, Strawberries, Sea, Eye, Herrings, Wood.

PAGE.

48. Baby Hunting, Milking, Rabbit, Baby, Inn.

49. Jack, Cock, Horse, Sword, Scabbard, Saddle, Spurs, Switches.

50. Marbles, Tops, Props, Jacket, Breeches, Rose, Violet, Pinks, Yew.

51. Rock, Baby, Ewer, Cradle, Nobleman, Queen, Lady, Ring, Drummer, Drums, King.

52. Gill, Hill, Pail, Water, Fell Down, Crown, Gill, Tumbling.

53. Chimney, Sweep, Awl, Top, Ladder, Rope, Chimney Sweep.

54. Boys, Girls, Moon, Supper, Sleep, Playfellows, Street.

55. Old Woman, Hill, Knot, Apples, Pies, Woman.

56. Lady Bird, Lady Bird, Fly, A Way, Home, Ewer, House is on Fire, Ewer, Children, Will Burn.

ROLLO'S TOUR IN EUROPE.

F. A. Brown & Co.
Publishers, Boston.

PRICE PER VOLUME, FIFTY CENTS.

HURRAH FOR THE LITTLE FOLKS!

CHANDLER'S

PAPER DOLLS,

OF THE

LATEST PARIS FASHIONS.

No. 1.—Carrie, with her Dresses and Bonnets.
No. 2.—Alice, with her Dresses and Bonnets.
No. 3.—Charlie, with a Wardrobe of Five changes, and Hats to match.
No. 4.—Little Fairy Lightfoot, the Dancing Girl, with Beautiful Dresses.
No. 5.—Betty the Milk-maid and all her Pets.
No. 6.—Jack and his Holiday Companions.
No. 7.—May Queen and Shepherdess.

PUBLISHED BY

FRED'K A. BROWN & CO.,

29 CORNHILL, BOSTON,

And for Sale by Booksellers generally.

2

FRED'K A. BROWN & CO.,

29 Cornhill, Boston,

PUBLISH THE

GOOD LITTLE PIG'S LIBRARY,

WHICH WILL BE COMPLETED AS FAST AS POSSIBLE.

THERE WILL BE TWELVE VOLUMES, AND ALL OUR LITTLE FRIENDS MUST CERTAINLY HAVE A SET.

Number 1.

REMARKABLE HISTORY OF FIVE LITTLE PIGS.
40 Illustrations.

Number 2.

THE WONDERFUL HISTORY OF THREE LITTLE KITTENS WHO LOST THEIR MITTENS. 8 Illustrations.

Number 3.

MISTER FOX. 8 Illustrations.

Number 4.

THE FROG WHO WOULD A WOOING GO. 17 Illustrations.

Number 5.

THE GOOD LITTLE PIG'S PICTURE ALPHABET.
30 Illustrations.

OTHER VOLUMES WILL FOLLOW SOON.